Lighthouses of Engl[...]

PORTLAND BILL

by

Martin Boyle

and

Ken Trethewey

B & T Publications

Printed by Cedar Press (Southern) Ltd.

PUBLISHED BY B & T PUBLICATIONS,

10 Orchard Way, Highfield, Southampton.

Hampshire SO17 1RD.

International Standard Book Number

ISBN 1-901043-01-0

International Standard Serial Number

ISSN 1363 8009

Printed by Cedar Press (Southern) Ltd.

Lighthouses of Southern England

1. Portland Bill

2. Anvil Point

3. Hurst Point

4. Needles

5. St. Catherine's Point

6. Nab Tower

Hampshire

Southampton

West Sussex

Dorset

3

4

5

6

1

2

Isle of Wight

SPECIAL ACKNOWLEDGEMENT

The authors gratefully acknowledge the invaluable help of the Corporation of Trinity House, its Publications Officer and Media Director, its Director of Engineering and his exceptional Staff, with the full co-operation of the Master and Elder Brethren.

Photo by K. Trethewey

PORTLAND BILL

Location: Peninsula Island near Weymouth, Dorset
Lat/Long: 50.31.03N - 02.27.03W
No. on Admiralty list of lights: 0294
Present lighthouse constructed: 1906
Designer: Sir Thomas Matthews
Builder: Wakeham Bros. Ltd., Plymouth
Tower: Purbeck Stone
Focal plane of light: 140ft (42.67m) AHWST
Light first visible: 11 January 1906
Corporation: Trinity House
Monarch at time of construction: Edward VII (1901-1910)

Connected to the Dorset mainland by the notorious Chesil Bank causeway, is the peninsula island of Portland. On one side is West Bay and on the other Weymouth Bay. Three miles to the south-east of Portland Bill, the extreme point of the island, lies the Shambles sandbank. Where the tide meets between these two points it is known as the deadly Portland Race. This area of strong currents has dragged numerous ships, their seafarers and cargoes to a watery grave.

Portland's main claim to fame is its famous limestone quarries and the stone produced for many historic buildings. Following the Great Fire of London in 1666, architect Sir Christopher Wren insisted that St. Paul's Cathedral should be built with Portland stone. John Smeaton used it for the internal masonry of his Eddystone lighthouse in 1759. One of the biggest projects using this limestone, was the Portland Breakwater. Grove Prison, formerly a hard labour prison, used its first intake of convicts to quarry the limestone for this project. Work for the Portland Breakwater officially began on the 25th July 1849, when the Consort of Queen Victoria, Prince Albert, set the first stone. A block of Whitbed stone from Portland's Suckthumb Quarry at Weston was carved with a Coat of Arms and an inscription that reads:

"From this spot, on the 25th July 1849 His Royal Highness Prince Albert, Consort to Queen Victoria, sank the first stone of this breakwater. Upon the same spot, Albert Edward, Prince of Wales, on the 10th of August 1872, laid the last stone and declared the work completed. THESE ARE IMPERIAL WORKS AND WORTHY KINGS." [1]

On completion of the breakwater, a total of 5,731,376 tons of Portland stone had been quarried by hundreds of convicts over a period of 23 years [2].

Most of Portland's history revolves around its treacherous coastline which has claimed the lives of numerous mariners and whetted its appetite on countless ships. Considering the volume of shipping that passes this peninsula, it seems strange that there was not a lighthouse until the early 18th century.

The first application to build a lighthouse at Portland was made to the Parliament of Charles II in 1668, by Sir John Clayton. Of the many petitions he put forward in respect of private lighthouse ownership, this was one that was strongly opposed by Trinity House. From the application records of Corton, Cromer (Foulness), Flamborough Head lighthouses and the attempted Nore lightship project, it is clear that Clayton was personally disliked by the Elders of Trinity House. Sir John's petition for the Portland lighthouse Patent, was however granted, despite the objections put forward by the Corporation. The Elders must have shared a private smile when it became clear that the contents of the Patent insisted that only voluntary contributions for the upkeep of the lighthouse could be taken from ship owners. When Sir John Clayton failed to reach a suitable agreement with the merchants and shipowners, he cancelled his project and surrendered his Patent [3].

Thirty years later the need for a lighthouse at Portland became an important issue following an increase in the number of ships being wrecked around this Dorset peninsula. In 1699, Sir John Coryton, a London businessman with connections with the merchants of Weymouth, applied for a Letter-Patent to erect a lighthouse with the right to collect compulsory dues from shipping for its upkeep. Again, Trinity House strongly objected to the proposal on the grounds that there was no need for a light and a levy would only be an unwarranted burden on ship owners. The application was refused [3].

A year later in 1700, Captain William Holman from Weymouth, a privateer for William III, applied for a Letter-Patent to build two lighthouses at Portland. His application was backed by numerous merchants and ship owners, along with the Weymouth Corporation, but once again Trinity House voiced strong opposition. The objection was not only the financial burden on shipping but, more importantly, they insisted that the location of the lights would assist the King's enemies at a time of war. This application was also refused [3].

For a further 15 years, the Weymouth Corporation, local merchants and shipowners continued to petition Trinity House for a lighthouse at Portland. Trinity House finally withdrew its opposition and, on the face of it, actually appeared to agree with the need for a lighthouse. In fact, the Elder Brethren did not want the lighthouse to pass into in private ownership because they realised the Corporation would lose the lucrative profits from the venture.

Trinity House applied for a Patent for the Portland lights in January 1716, which was formally acknowledged in principle by the Parliament of George I. With this agreement, Trinity House posted for tenders and accepted a proposal from the Dorset consortium of William Borrett, Francis Browne and a Weymouth builder called Charles Langrishe. On the 12th February 1716, Trinity House issued a lease to the consortium which allowed them to erect two lighthouses at Portland for a rental period of 61 years at £100 per year and the right to collect compulsory dues from shipping at "*1/4 penny per ton from English ships and 1/2 penny from Foreigners.*" When the Corporation received its official Letter-Patent, a clause was added which allowed it to collect a percentage of the levies paid to the lease-holders as an attendance fee [4].

On the 29th September 1716, Charles Langrishe and Francis Browne completed the construction of the Portland lights and most of the ancillary buildings [3]. Keepers accommodation and storage units were finally in position by the end of November. Both lighthouses had glazed coal-fired lanterns that required the use of leather bellows which the keepers pumped during the night to keep the flame bright. For nearly ten years access to these lighthouses was along virtually non-existent mud tracks. Along these muddy lanes the coal was hauled by horse and cart, then stockpiled in a field which became known as '*Coal Lands*' [3].

Chistopher Comben's appointment as assistant keeper for the Portland lights in 1721 began a family of keepers which spanned nearly 200 years. During one period all the keepers were Combens, and local people referred to the Portland lights as "*Combens Lighthouse*" [5].

During the early part of the 19th century, the lack of seamen led to the re-introduction of impressment. Very few men were exempt from this law which allowed officers and navy personnel to arrest a person on the street, in a tavern or even at home and force them to serve on board His Majesty's ships. Trinity House was given authority by the Lord High Admiral to issue exemption certificates to all their lighthouse keepers. In1806, Robert Comben was appointed assistant keeper for the Portland lights and was issued with his official letter of exemption. It read:

"These are to CERTIFY, whom it may concern, that the bearer hereof ROBERT COMBEN (whose age & description are hereunder stated), is employ'd by the Corporation of Trinity House of DEPTFORD STROND as ASSISTANT KEEPER of the PORTLAND LIGHTS; and it being of the utmost importance to the safety of all His Majesty's ships and Vessels as well those of His subjects and others navigating past the coasts of this Kingdom, that all LIGHT-HOUSES should be constantly maintained with the utmost care and attention.

The said Corporation do hereby make it their Request, to all Officers and other employ'd in the impressing of seamen, not in any wise to molest or interrupt the said ROBERT COMBEN while passing from Portland to Weymouth in quest of necessaries for his family or otherwise employed in the service of the said Lights."

"Robert Comben, aged 24 years, 5 ft 9 ins High, and wears his own black hair."

"Given under the seal of the CORPORATION OF TRINITY HOUSE at LONDON, this Fourth Day of September 1806 (signed) Joseph Cotton Deputy Master" [6]

In the Parish listings dated 25th November 1836, there is a record of *"Richard Comben of the Light-House"* as one of the signatories who voted in the official Trustee members who would be responsible for a piece of land in Southwell that had been bought with contributions from the local people, as a site for the new Methodist Church [6].

The last Comben to serve as keeper at Portland was in 1906 and this ended 185 years of a family tradition. It must be remembered that those who came into the service as lighthouse keepers during the late 18th century always preserved a tremendous loyalty to their jobs. For these men this was not just a means of employment, this was a way of life [5].

After Charles Langrishe completed the building of a road to the Portland lighthouses, the cost was found to have exceeded the original estimate. The consortium decided there must be a streamlining of their overheads, but at times the lighthouses were not kept to the required standard. Many ship owners complained to the Elders of Trinity House, during the winter months of 1751, who in turn made representations to the Consortium. Although assurances were given by the Consortium, complaints continued to be made by ship owners for nearly twelve months.

In September 1752, two Trinity House Brethren sailed to Portland to carry out a full survey. They reported that *"it was nigh on two hours after sunset before any light appeared in either lighthouse"*. A closer investigation of the two lighthouses by the Elders revealed, *"both lanthorns are of a distressed state from the absence of polishing"*. Trinity House reacted by threatening to cancel the lease for the lights because there was an obvious breach of the agreement, *"to ensure a proper light for the safety of navigation"*. It was pointed out by Trinity House to the Consortium, that if the matter was not resolved immediately, the lease would be revoked with no possible claim for compensation. Charles Langrishe replaced much of the glazing to the lanterns of both lights by the following November [3].

When the descendants of the Borrett, Browne and Langrishe consortium applied for the renewal of their lease in August 1777 it was refused. On the day that Trinity House was due to take over the two Portland lights, two Elder Brethren sent to officiate the handing over of ownership were refused entry. Objections had been put forward in respect of a clause in the lease that stated, *"the lessees shall peaceably and quietly leave and yield up the lighthouses, buildings and roads, without a penny claim for compensation from the Corporation"*. In a local court a jury upheld the original agreement on the grounds that the triple partnership of Borrett, Browne and Langrishe had willingly signed the terms of the lease, so therefore it was legally binding.

Trinity House continued to use the existing Portland lighthouses for a further ten years but numerous ship owners complained that they were barely visible and often confusing because of their location.

During the summer months of 1788, Trinity House sent their Consultant Engineer, Samuel Wyatt, to supervise a remodernisation programme for the Portland high light. This involved the removal of the existing coal fired lantern and replacing it with a new unit with oil lamps. The new lantern was made from copper with *"the finest quality plate glass"* set into its frame [3].

Portland high light was fitted with Argand oil lamps and would be the first in Britain to use this invention. For this lighthouse there were fourteen lamps in two rows of seven, each with a circular cotton wick $^3/_4$ inch (18 mm) in diameter. Highly polished square metal reflectors were fitted and in August 1788 the tower was relit.

The Portland Lighthouses after re-building in 1788 (Whittock)

On completion of the high light, Trinity House asked various builders to tender for a contract to build a new low light at Portland and to demolish the existing 1716 tower. The tender from a Weymouth builder, William Johns, was accepted and in February 1789 he commenced the building of the new tower designed by Samuel Wyatt. Foundations for the new low light were sited further to the east of the existing tower so that it would provide a navigational reference during the day for ships using the English Channel, or into the Portland Roads, and safely clear of the Shambles Sandbanks. William Johns and his workforce built the new 63 ft (19.2 m) low lighthouse from stone obtained at the local quarry. At its base it was 20 ft (6.09 m) in diameter and tapered to 10 ft (3.05 m) in diameter at the cornice below the lantern. The doorway and window openings were in a gothic style and above the entrance door, Trinity House erected a marble plaque to commemorate the building of the tower. It reads [5]:

"For
The Direction and Comfort
of NAVIGATORS
for
The Benefit and Security
of COMMERCE:
A lasting Memorial
of BRITISH HOSPITALITY
To All Nations.
This Light House was erected
By the ancient Corporation
of TRINITY - HOUSE
of Deptford Strond
in 1789
Distance from the
Cliff 1608 Feet"

On entering the lighthouse, access to the lamp room was by a Portland stone spiral staircase edged with an ornate iron balustrade. The lantern was made of heavy copper and similar in design to the one installed on the high tower. Plate glass was fitted to the lantern and six Argand oil lamps were positioned inside with silvered glass reflectors. Plano-convex lenses were fitted by Thomas Rogers, the inventor, and his partner George Robinson, an optical expert. When these lenses were first supplied, they each cost £50, a considerable price in 1789[7].

When the new Portland low light was brought into service in October 1789, it became the first lighthouse in the world to use magnifying optical lenses. In *"Hutchinson's, History and Antiquities of the County of Dorset (1881)"* he wrote: *"so well did they succeed that it often appeared that the lights were visible till the distance was so great as to sink them* (the ships) *below the horizon".* Trinity House Archives record the range at between 18 and 19 nautical miles, but even this exceeded the expectations of the Corporation by 4 miles.

The two Portland lights were 1509 ft (460 m) apart, with the high light 210 ft 64 m) above high water. On several occasions the latter was reported to be shrouded in sea mist, but on a clear night ship Captains stated that its beam was visible on the horizon as they approached the area. The low light was 136 ft (41.5 m) above high water with a recorded visible distance of 15 nautical miles.

Near the end of December 1789, William Johns handed his final accounts for the completed Portland contract to the Corporation. It amounted to £2000 and also proved the skills of his workforce by being below budget and completed within 10 months - 4 weeks early. In the Corporation's minutes for this period Samuel Wyatt, the designer of the lighthouse, commented on the workmanship and his pleasure at its early completion [3].

By the latter part of the 18th century, there was a dramatic increase in sea trade. Much of this business brought about a rapid expansion of Portland as a major naval port. But the powerful new lights failed to reduce the number of ships being wrecked. In 1795 a fleet sailing under Admiral Christian suffered a disasterous loss on the Shambles Reef and the lights were subsequently fiercely criticised by the Admiral as being totally useless. The

Elder Brethren responded by issuing a statement that read, *"lights do not prevent shipwrecks, they only provide a navigational light"*. In a letter to the Admiralty Inquiry Board the Elders wrote: *"If those who sail upon His Majesty's Seas fail to use the lights when passing, then a wrecking will occur"*. No details of the outcome of the inquiry into Admiral Christian's fleet have been found, which seems strange when Naval law classed the loss of a Kings ship *'by skillful means'* by its Master, as a criminal offence [8].

A threatened invasion by Napoleon's forces became real possibility in 1798 with Trinity House reluctantly allowing the Admiralty to install two 18 pound cannons on the Portland low light. The Corporation felt that this action was contrary to the humanitarian aims of the lights. This would be the only time during the Corporation's history that the Elders allowed their lighthouses to be armed for war [3].

During his tour of English lighthouses in 1801, Robert Stevenson, Engineer-in-Chief for the Commissioners of the Northern Lights, reported the Portland lighthouses, *"to be in a most excellent condition"*, but he did add a comment that he considered their present siting needed further investigation as they failed to adequately mark the Shambles Shoal. It would take until 1824 before this problem was addressed. In response to numerous requests from the Admiralty and concerned ship owners, Trinity House positioned two marker buoys over the Shambles Reef. One contained a large bell to provide an audible navigational aid [3].

By 1833 the Portland lights had become a very profitable business venture. In the Corporation's Annual Report for this period, a net yearly income of £2,300 was shown. With the rates of light dues set at one penny for English ships and two pence for foreign, this return gives a clear indication of the number of vessels that had passed these lights during this particular year.

A new optical apparatus was introduced to the Portland high light during the summer of 1836. James Walker, the Corporation's new Consultant Engineer, supervised the work carried out by Chance Brothers & Co. of Birmingham. This upgrading of the Portland lights, provided the area with two of the most powerful lights along the English coast [3].

Up to 1843 most shipping used the daylight hours to enter or leave the

Portland High Lighthouse, now Branscombe Lodge.
(Photo K. Trethewey).

harbours of Portland or Weymouth. For this reason Trinity House approached the Officer-in-Charge of Grove Prison for men to build a suitable daymark. By September 1844, a 30 ft (9.14 m) high obelisk had been erected. It is inscribed, simply, "T.H.1844" [7].

Apart from the introduction of a new ventilator system to each of the lights, nothing further was done to change their method of operation until 1856. At this time James Walker obtained the services of various local tradesmen to modernise the Portland low light. This involved the demolition of the existing dwellings and the construction of more suitable keepers quarters. Both the low and high lights were fitted with new optics and more efficient oil lamps designed by Augustin Fresnel. As the work progressed on the low light the Corporation decided to raise the high tower by 15 ft (4.57 m) in an attempt to increase the visible range of its light.On completion of the contract this work had cost a total of £1,050 [3]. One of the biggest problems for the Elders of Trinity house was the navigational difficulties caused by gas lights shining out from Grove Prison. This situation was causing confusion to shipping to such an extent, that the eastern profile of the Portland lights were completely obscured. Politics proved to be deadly slow in providing a solution. On one hand, the

Corporation insisted that the prison lights should be extinguished or shielded, but, on the other, the Officer-in-Charge of the prison was adamant that the lights were necessary for security reasons [3].

For 3 years the arguments continued between the Corporation and the Prison Authorities, during which time several ships were damaged or lost near the Shambles Reef. To overcome the problem Trinity House stationed its first lightship over the shoal. Conditions aboard this light-ship were extremely primitive and on occasions the red wooden-hulled vessel was almost capsized by the sea, but following its introduction this light-vessel provided a clear marking of the reef with its light at 38 ft (11.58 m) above high water and visible for a range of 10 nautical miles. Its distinctive recognition signal was one flash of 5 seconds, followed by an eclipse of 6 seconds. Its next sequence was one flash of 1.5 seconds and an eclipse of 17.5 seconds. A gong was installed as a fog warning system but its use must have been very limited[9].

In 1866, the Elder Brethren decided to completely rebuild the Portland towers for reasons of height and range of visibility. Both of the new towers were designed by James Nicholas Douglass on the recommendation of James Walker. Now known as Branscombe Lodge, the high tower was built as a two storey circular building. A substantial Portland stone plinth 17 ft 3 ins (5.26 m) in diameter provided the base foundation for the 35 ft (10.67 m) high tower. An ogee-shaped cornice formed the edge of the gallery, with a horizontal iron handrail and ornamental standards. Its helical lantern was designed by James Nicholas Douglass and manufactured by Chance Brothers of London [3].

The lantern for the Portland high light, was 13 ft 6 ins (4.11 m) in diameter. It was formed of an iron pedestal base 4 ft 6 ins (1.37 m) high, with its glazed section standing 10 ft6 ins (3.2 m) in height. This section was topped by a 3 ft 9 ins (1.14 m) high domed iron roof surmounted by a ball finial ventilator and weather vane. Inside, the lantern was a 1st order dioptric lens apparatus with its light source produced by a Wilkins 5-wicked oil lamp. Its flash operation was provided by a Wilkins and Son clockwork occulting mechanism. The recorded visible range for this light was 21 nautical miles and it was first lit in March 1867.

Old Portland Bill Lower Tower 1867
(Reproduced with kind permission of Trinity House)

Portland's low light, now known as Bay View, was similar in construction to the high light although 5 storeys high. This 75ft 3ins (22.94 m) high circular tower was built as an attachment to the 2 storey coastguard station. Its lantern and optical apparatus was of the same design and construction as its partner. Its recorded visible range was 18 nautical miles. The focal level for this light was 85 ft (25.9 m) above its foundation base. It was first officially lit in October 1867.

Both the high and low Portland stations had their own family quarters which housed three full-time keepers. Construction of the new dwellings and roadways to both lighthouses was completed in November 1869. It is interesting to note that the low light had a very special quality, the fertility of its soil. Members of the Comben family were proud of the fact that when other people were planting potatoes, they were digging their's up [2].

During the introduction of the Chance Brothers optics into the Portland lights, a law suit concerning their design reached the Dorchester Courts. Sir David Brewster insisted that he alone was the inventor and designer of the dioptric system. In 1866 he decided to take legal action to prove his right for the Patent. Prior to this he had corresponded with Thomas Milner Gibson at the Board of Trade on several occasions between 1861 and 1866, but the matter was unresolved and two weeks before the legal proceedings were due to commence he withdrew his claim. The protagonists agreed that the dioptric system had originally been invented by Augustin Fresnel and the design of the Portland optics had been based on the Fresnel system. After local papers reported Sir David Brewster's withdrawn court action his credibility was badly affected [10].

South-westerly gales often ravaged the coastline around Portland during the late 19th century, especially affecting ships under sail. Many of these vessels were driven helplessly on to the Chesil causeway or on the rocks around Portland Bill. In 1872 the keepers of the low light witnessed a single shipping incident involving more than 3000 people. On the night of the 25th November more people would die on land following the shipwreck than those who perished when it was blown ashore on Chesil Bank.

The iron sailing ship the ROYAL ADELAIDE was en route to Sydney from London. On board were the Master, Captain J.Hunter, 35 passengers and 32 crew. Her cargo consisted of numerous casks of spirits, wine and strong French liqueurs. As the ROYAL ADELAIDE approached Portland, a sudden south-westerly gale blew her off course and onto Chesil Bank. Local Coastguard and Customs men raced to her assistance, firing ropes onto the decks with Wyke Rockets. The passengers and crew were rescued by means of a crude chair made from a fruit basket and ropes attached to the main mast. Strangely, Captain Hunter was more concerned for his own safety and was the fourth person to be pulled ashore. This was noted by one of the Coastguards who reported seeing women and children huddling together on the ADELAIDE's wave-washed deck.

In the space of 20 minutes the ADELAIDE began to break up, but not before all the survivors were ashore. One of the last people to be rescued was the very obese wife of Assistant Steward Irons. Before she could get into the basket it was necessary for her to remove most of her clothes. After a great deal of difficulty, the Coastguards were able to pull her ashore, but when she landed it took a number of strong men to release her from the basket.

As the ADELAIDE broke up her cargo washed ashore and, within an hour, word of the free alcohol reached the local inhabitants. The Coastguards thought the approaching crowds were coming to help with the rescue, but instead they turned into a wild, uncontrollable mob of looters. Two hours later, Chesil beach was a mass of drunken men and women, fighting over the free liquor. Many couples were having sex and after a short while the shore was littered with people who had passed out drunk. There was nothing the rescuers could do and, fearing for their own safety, they led the survivors to the security of the Customs House in Portland Harbour.

Early the following morning the local militia arrived at Chesil Bank where they found 20 of the wreckers dead from alcohol poisoning: only six had died when the ADELAIDE ran aground.

The owners of the ADELAIDE decided not to prosecute the looters as they felt it would not be in the best interests of the local Customs and Coastguards. The last thing the shipowners wanted was the withdrawal of Coastguards services as this would leave Portland Harbour unprotected [8].

In 1883 the wooden-hulled SHAMBLES lightship was replaced by a new iron light-vessel. The crew consisted of the Master, four Able seamen and three lamp lighters. This 180ton unpowered ship had a lantern which contained eight large oil lamps. During the two months tour of duty, the conditions for the crew were very confined and extremely monotonous[2].

Shambles Lightship (Reproduced with kind permission of Trinity House).

Until 1900, roads to Portland were mud tracks mainly due to the continual use of steam traction engines used to bring supplies to the area. Most of the oil for the Portland lights was carried on board their trailers to Castletown where it was then transported by horse and cart to the lighthouses. Only on rare occasions had it been possible for Trinity House to supply the oil from ships due to the dangerous rocks and seas around the coast [3].

Following the tremendous gales and storms of 1901 when about 15 ships were wrecked around Portland, Trinity House instructed its Engineer-in-Chief, Sir Thomas Matthews, to prepare plans, specifications and estimates for a new lighthouse. By January 1903 the project was ready to commence but the chosen site was on the common land of Bill Point. In June many of the local residents met at the George Inn in Easton Square to discuss the proposals. This involved arranging compensation to the community because of the extinction of their common rights, once the Corporation had acquired the land. Trinity House Elders who attended the meeting pointed out that the sites of the existing lighthouses were no longer suitable and the present towers unable to house the new equipment and optical apparatus. Agreement was reached and in October the construction company, Wakeham Brothers Ltd., from Plymouth, came in a convoy of traction engines across the rough roads to Bill Point to commence their contract [3].

Wakeham Brothers started with the preparation of the tower foundations. This required an excavation into the rocky ground, 7 ft (2.1 m) deep, 10 ft 6 ins (3.2 m) wide and 34 ft (10.36 m) in diameter. This was subsequently filled with concrete to form the ground floor level of the tower at 26 ft 2 ins (7.98 m) above HWST. On this substantial footing were set the 4 ft 3 ins (1.3 m) thick purbeck stones which formed the 30 ft (9.14 m) diameter base walls of the tower. Unlike conventional lighthouses the walls of the Portland Bill tower tapered internally as well as externally, to a height of 99 ft 4 ins (30.28 m). Above this level were set the 5 ft 6 ins (1.68 m) high moulded gallery stones.

In sections of about 8 ft (2.44 m) lifts, Wakeham Brothers erected a wooden scaffold around Portland tower. This scaffold brought sightseers from

Wooden Scaffold erected by Wakeham Brothers. (Reproduced with the kind permission of Trinity House)

miles around, many believing this seemingly unsteady structure would soon collapse. One of the construction workers commented to a local newspaper reporter, *"The only time we'll worry about our rocking scaffold, is when it stops moving"*. When the reporter asked what he meant, the worker replied, *"If that happens, we're on the way down"* [3].

After the first course of stones for the Portland tower was set in position the 21 ft 6 in(6.58 m) diameter ground floor of the lighthouse was formed. Above this level the walls were carried up to the underside of the gallery stones, in 58 courses of masonry 1 ft 8 ins (552 mm) thick. At this level the walls were 2 ft 8 ins (806 mm) thick and the external diameter of the tower 19 ft 5 ins (5.92 m).

After the heavy moulded gallery stones were set into position on top of the Portland tower it was 23 ft 3 ins (7.08 m) in diameter and 104 ft 10 ins (31.96 m) in height. The internal section at this level formed the 14 ft 2 ins (4.31 m) diameter service room. Around the perimeter of gallery stones was erected a 3 ft 6 ins (1.07 m) high, 3 tier tubular steel handrail, with its standards leaded into position.

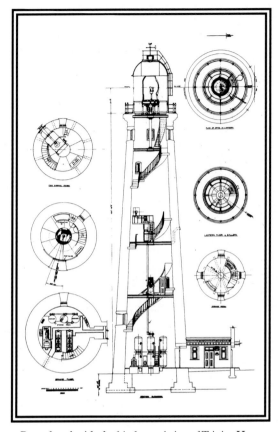

Reproduced with the kind permission of Trinity House

The interior of the Portland lighthouse was divided into five levels. The ground floor contained the oil tanks and workshop. From this level the paraffin was pumped under pressure to smaller tanks in the service room. A further pump pressurised the oil which was then fed to the lamps in the lantern room above. In the centre of the service room, was erected a 1 ft (305mm) diameter hollow steel stanchion. This stanchion was used to support the weight of the optical apparatus and hold the drive weight for the clockwork mechanism. The floor of this service room was constructed from a network of 1 ft (305 mm) deep rolled steel joists, surfaced with 6 ins (152 mm) of reinforced concrete. The 3 ft (914 mm) diameter base plate of the stanchion was bolted through the floor and onto the steel joists. A further plate was fixed to the top of the stanchion which was bolted to the underside of the joists supporting the lantern floor. This floor was of similar construction, but without a concrete slab. Instead a centralised chequered steel plate, 18mm thick and 8 ft (2.44 m) in diameter, was bolted onto the joists. Around the perimeter of this plate were segments of iron grating that filled in the remaining area of the lantern room floor.

The crowning feature was its Douglass designed helical lantern. This unit was manufactured by Chance Brothers of Birmingham who were also commissioned to supply and erect all of the optical apparatus, rotating drive mechanism and fog signal unit. This particular lantern was constructed out of a gun-metal framing with a copper clad roof. It was 15 ft 6 ins(4.72 m) in diameter and 25 ft (7.62 m) to the top of its drum ventilator. Like most lanterns it arrived in a kit form packed into large wooden crates. The first section of this unit consisted of a 4 ft 6 ins (1.37 m) high iron pedestal base which had specially designed ventilators built to its walls. These hit-and-miss type ventilators provided a constant flow of air over the internal face of the lantern to prevent condensation. On to the pedestal base was erected the 10 ft 4 ins(3.15 m) high glazed section, which was topped by a 5 ft 9 in (1.75 m) high domed roof. On to this roof was fixed a 6 ft 2 ins (1.88 m) diameter drum ventilator, 4 ft 5 ins (1.35 m) in height. Above this unit was erected a lightning conductor and arrow-shaped weather vane.

Douglass helical lantern
(Photo by K. Trethewey)

The heart of the Portland lighthouse was its majestic 1st order dioptric lens apparatus. This Chance Brothers creation was almost 10 ft (3.05 m) high and 6 ft 8 ins (2.03 m) in diameter. It stood on a specially designed revolving pedestal base, 6 ft (1.83 m) in height and nearly 7 ft (2.1 m) in diameter. This particular optic floated in a tray of mercury which provided a virtual friction-free bed for the 3.75 ton unit. The focal level for this optic was set at 140 ft (42.67 m) above HWST [11].

A Matthews incandescent mantle burner was the light source for the new Portland Bill lighthouse. This large lamp was devised by Sir Thomas Matthews based on an invention of Arthur Kitson. Paraffin gas vapour was obtained by heating the pressurised mineral oil in a retort below the mantle. A methylated

21

Clockwork mechanism for rotating lighthouse optic. (Photo by K. Trethewey)

spirit burner beneath the retort, was used to provide the initial heat source. After a short time the paraffin turned into a white gas which the keeper lit on top of the silk mantle. Compared to the standard wick lamps, this incandescent burner effectively trebled the light source value. In terms of consumption, this system virtually halved the quantity of fuel normally used for the same period of operation. The intensity of the light through the optics was equivalent to about 3.37 million candle power, providing a visible range of nearly 18 nautical miles [3].

A clockwork mechanism was employed to rotate the optic with the power obtained by a heavy weight descending inside of the hollow steel stanchion. Attached to the mechanism was a small gearbox which allowed a slower rate of descent. The previous drive ratio for similar units was normally about 1 ft (305 mm) per hour. This new Chance Brothers gearbox let the mechanism run for nearly 18 hours, before the weight needed rewinding to its starting position.

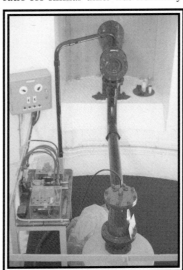

Fog Signal equipment from inside lighthouse (Photo by K. Trethewey)

Access to each of the levels inside the Portland Bill lighthouse, was by means of a purbeck stone geometrical staircase built into the walls of the tower. This staircase wound its way to the service room where an open-plan steel flight of steps gave access to the lantern room. On the second floor was erected a powerful diaphone fog unit positioned at 72 ft (21.96m) above ground level. This fog system was devised by Chance Brothers and based upon a similar principle as the siren. The only difference is that there were no revolving discs inside the diaphone. Instead, a piston powered by compressed air, forced out the confined air behind a series of slits and produced a distinct melodious sound. The length of this note was controlled by adjusting the distance the piston had to travel inside its tubular casing. The air supply for this fog unit was supplied by a 6 ins (152 mm) steel pipe, fed from an air compressor on the ground floor. This in turn, was driven by a pair of steam engines; one in operation at any one time, whose exhausts exited through the wall of the tower.

On the first floor of the Portland lighthouse a red sector light was installed which covered the Shambles Reef. This fixed light had a similar arrangement for its light source and a 2nd order dioptric lens. Its focal plane was set at 77 ft (23.57 m) below the main light, or 63ft 8 ins (19.41 m) above HWST. The light is viewed from the sea, at a bearing of 280°. The intensity of its light was 11,000 candle power with a visible range of about 13 nautical miles.

To the rear of the Portland lighthouse was erected a two storey dwelling. This substantial building can only be described as architecturally majestic. It was connected to the tower by a 19 ft (5.79 m) long by 8 ft 3 ins (2.5 m) wide single storey corridor with a flat roof edged with a moulded parapet wall. The ground floor of this dwelling was almost 56 ft (17 m) long and 35 ft (10.67 m) wide. All the external structural walls were of solid purbeck stone 18 ins

The majestic keepers quarters at Portland. (Photo by K. Trethewey)

(457 mm) thick, with the internal masonry of 12 ins (305 mm) thick locally made bricks. On this level were such amenities as a sitting room, living room, large kitchen, scullery, wood and coal store and an earth closet. All these rooms were duplicated to form an east and a west wing to the dwelling. The upper floor was smaller and contained all the bedrooms. It ran from the front line of the single storey corridor for a distance of 45 ft 4 ins (13.82 m). After this the remaining area over the ground floor structure was formed into a flat roof, similar in design to the corridor. Access to the upper floor was provided by two independent internal staircases. Each of these spacious two storey apartments was originally for two full-time keepers and their families. A relief keeper covered the extra duty periods, but he lived in the nearby village [12].

A large car park was built at the back of the Portland station, originally intended for the personnel working or visiting the lighthouse, but within two years of the light being built, it was taken over by the public who came to view the lighthouse.

On the 11th January 1906 Principal Keeper Comben and Assistant Keeper Taylor moved their families and personal belongings into the Portland Bill lighthouse station. At 1630 the same evening these keepers officially lit the lights for the first time. Its main light had a recognition signal of Gp Fl (4) every 20 seconds. The sequence provided was an unusual feature because it allowed the light to gradually change from one flash to four from 221° to 244° and a pattern of four flashes up to 117°. After this the flashing sequence changed from four flashes to one flash up to a bearing of 141°. Between 141° to 221° the light was obscured by polished copper panels inside the lantern [3].

One of the last tasks to be carried out by Wakeham Brothers was the facing of the lighthouse with sand and cement rendering. They also painted the lantern white and a central 33 ft(10 m) wide band around the tower in the distinctive red livery of the station. The remainder of the tower was painted white. This paintwork was to ensure the lighthouse provided a prominent daymark for shipping. The total cost for the Portland contract, was £13,000.

In 1907, as part of its agreement for the loss of common rights at Portland Bill, Trinity House kept its promise and auctioned the Old High and Low lighthouses. This auction was carried out at the George Inn in Easton Square.

Local advertisements were posted in various papers and numerous shop windows, along with the statutory requirement of placing the information in the National Press [13]. The advert read:

"Wonderfully suited for consumptives in winter, and convalescent in other seasons. In the fertile gardens of the Lower lighthouse, potatoes are dug when people elsewhere are thinking of planting."

The expected numbers of intended buyers failed to materialise and only the High lighthouse was sold for £405. Previously agreeing a minimum of £425, Trinity House withdrew the Lower light house when the bidding reached only £400. The High lighthouse became known as 'Branscombe Lodge' with its own stables to the west. The Lower lighthouse remained virtually unchanged until it was taken over by a local ornithology society and used as a bird observatory. These days it is better known as 'Bay View' and is still attached to the Portland Coastguard station [3].

During the first World war, Portland Bill became a prominent observation post for the Admiralty and one of the most protected stations along the south coast of England. Its location close to the Portland Naval base made this area a prime target for German U-boats. This underwater menace was causing havoc with shipping to such an extent that on the 4th November 1914 the 14,000 ton battleship, HMS HOOD, was deliberately sunk to block the southern entrance to Portland Harbour [8].

Between 1914 and 1918 the Portland light was reduced to half power and only lit for the passing of Allied shipping. During this time the Portland Naval base saw a continuous flow of coasters from Newcastle or Wales bringing coal for the hungry boilers of British warships. These coasters formed up to 5 mile long convoys, which made perilous voyages down the Bristol and St. George's Channels before a second wave of German U-boats played havoc with the slow moving vessels using the English Channel [8].

Up to the early 1940s, the operation of Portland Bill lighthouse remained virtually unchanged apart from a new David Hood mantle lamp. This improved system was similar to the Matthews burner except that the methylated heater had become part of the lamp. This effectively concentrated the heat source safely and without a premature ignition of the paraffin gas. This lamp also had a new type of mantle which expanded to a ball shape twice its normal size. This autoform mantle increased the light source by about 40% [3].

In July 1942 the original coke burning steam engines and belt driven air compressor were removed from the Portland station. The ground floor area of the tower was modernised and divided into an independent engine room and workshop. New diesel powered motors were installed, which required a circulating water tank to cool the engines. The new air compressor was fitted with three pressurised air storage receivers which fed the diaphone fog unit.

Accepted as a simple system these days, the Portland engines and air compressor came into operation automatically by means of a control unit that had a pressure valve connected to a solenoid starter. The main cooling tank was built outside the lighthouse with the pipework under the corridor floor and out through the wall. This large open-ended galvanised tank was surfaced with an iron grating and during cold weather it either gave off clouds of steam or froze over. Various forms of anti-freeze were used but within 10 years, most of the pipework and large section of the tank had corroded [14].

On the 5th May 1952, Philip W.Hunt, the Corporation's Engineer-in-Chief, supervised the modernisation of the Portland lights to electrical operation. A mains electricity supply was brought to the station along with numerous complaints from the local residents because they were not allowed to share the supply. Trinity House strongly believed that any additional loading on its supply might cause the lights to fail. Much of the new equipment at Portland was supplied by Chance Brothers whose business now extended more widely than just the original lanterns and optical apparatus. The main light had a Type 'B' electric lamp exchanger with two filament bulbs. Its primary light source was a 100 volt, 3 KW lamp that was 1 ft 2ins (355 mm) long with its glass globe nearly 8 ins (203 mm) in diameter. A smaller stand-by lamp was incorporated on this exchanger that operated on 50 volts with a power output of 500 watts. Compared to the main bulb this lamp was considerably smaller. A similar arrangement was installed in the subsidiary light. These bulbs were 100 volt, 500 watt and 50 volt with a 250 watt outputs respectively [15].

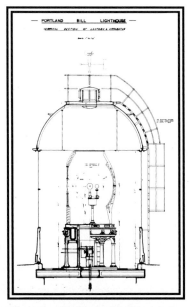

When the light source was changed in the lantern room the Portland keepers were pleased to see a Chance Brothers electric motor installed which would automatically rewind the heavy drive weight. Although a stand-by manual winder was incorporated there is no record that it was ever used. In accordance with the usual practice of Trinity House, stand-by generators were installed in the engine room. One of the existing diesel motors was used to power this generator. The subsequent intensity

Reproduced with the kind permission of Trinity House

of the Portland light provided a visible range of about 29 nautical miles. On several occasions the Masters of ships reported that the Corporation's calculations must be wrong. They said that, although their ships were well below the horizon, the glow of the flashing Portland lights could still be clearly seen [3].

Within five years moisture was causing problems inside the lighthouse. Most of these difficulties came from the deterioration of the existing diesel engines and numerous leaks in the pipework from the circulating water cooler system. A break in the mains supply was caused on a few occasions, combined with a failure of the stand-by generators to cut in. Trinity House instructed its engineering department to

Electric lamp changer (Photo K. Trethewey).

27

implement the necessary work and by the 1st November 1957 this problem had been resolved. The existing cooling system was modernised with the piping and tanks changed to copper. The original tank was removed and a purbeck casing built around a new copper unit [16].

Not only was the cooling system at Portland replaced, but new Lister diesel engines were installed, along with a smaller, yet more powerful generators. Because of the excess moisture, much of the existing electrical cabling had to be replaced. Several extractor fans were fitted which automatically came into operation if the moisture level was too high.

By the early 1960s the existing accommodation at Portland Bill was no longer suitable. Philip Hunt was asked to design a new two storey residential block to the rear of the lighthouse. By the 4th March 1963, this building was home for two more full-time keepers and their families. When these keepers arrived at the station, the numbers of this small isolated community rose to 19 people. While the building work was in progress on the new dwelling the

New quarters built to rear of station. (Photo by K. Trethewey)

existing residential block was modernised. This involved the introduction of central heating, running hot and cold water, enamelled cast iron baths and luxurious water closets [17].

In 1964 high powered mercury vapour lamps were introduced to the Portland station but with short-lived popularity. Although these bulbs provided an exceptionally bright light they were extremely expensive for the period of time they remained in service. Trinity House reverted to the original tungsten filament bulbs and put the matter down to experience. During this time the existing air compressor was removed and replaced by a new unit with its own built-in motor. This made one of the diesel engines redundant, which was also taken out, then replaced by a second generator [3].

Near the end of 1964, Trinity House was informed of the dangers involved with the use of mercury. Even at a relatively low temperature it was reported that mercury formed a very toxic gas. Tests were carried out on several keepers who had been stationed in lighthouses with mercury flotation trays and found the level of mercury in their blood stream to be higher than expected. Within 12 months of this information becoming available, Trinity House not only implemented new working procedures for keepers but had the mercury removed from all its stations. At Portland this involved the careful removal of about three quarters of a ton of mercury. A new precision roller bearing bed was installed with the optic, turned by two electric motors [3].

By the beginning of 1970 technology was advancing at a rapid pace. New radio equipment for controlling the nearby Lanby station (which replaced the Shambles light-vessel) was installed. AB Pharos Marine UK Ltd, (formerly AGA) implemented many modifications to the lighthouse, which included the installation of a new three position lamp-changer with automatic operation. Much of the existing meteorological equipment was changed and a steel access ladder to reach these units was erected on the side of the lantern. The original drum ventilator was removed and a modern ball finial system introduced. Most of the electrical wiring was renewed and brought up to the required safety standard. Automatic fog sensors were installed on the handrail of the gallery which would now control the operation of the diaphone [3].

Among the last remaining keepers at Portland Bill, there were two principals and three assistant members of staff. Principal keeper, Tony John Homewood, joined Trinity House on the 18th April 1966 and was originally stationed at Lynmouth Foreland lighthouse. On the 8th September 1993, he transferred to Portland Bill following the automation of his former lighthouse. His off-duty associate was Lawrence Walker, who joined Trinity House on the 7th September 1970. He transferred to Portland Bill on the 1st May 1975. Because this station required two principal keepers, they were both promoted to these positions on the 11th September 1989.

One assistant keeper was Michael Hall, who joined Trinity House on the 18th March 1974 and became part of the team at Portland Bill on the 8th January 1990. Another, Paul Martin Copson, joined Trinity House on the 10th December 1979. He took up his position at Portland Bill on the 1st July 1989. Gordon Dickinson was the only member of the team who was a local man, joining it and Trinity House on the 1st June 1981.

In 1992 the preparations began to automate the Portland Bill lighthouse. This project was completed in 1996. After the generations of lighthouse keepers who have tended the Portland station, this automation programme meant people leaving somewhere which was not only their place of work, but their home. So what will become of these friendly and helpful keepers who have spent hours of their time showing interested members of the public around this historical lighthouse? All of these men and women will be found other positions of employment within the Corporation, but when they reach retirement age no-one will replace them.

Although the Portland Bill lighthouse is still monitored and maintained by Trinity House, the keepers quarters and other buildings will be turned into a maritime museum. This responsibility is vested with Weymouth Council, whose Leisure and Entertainments Department rightly believes that Portland Bill should remain a special tourist attraction as part of our maritime heritage.

Hand drawn picture of Portland Bill.
(Reproduced with the kind permission of Trinity House)

REFERENCES
1. Transcript taken from plaque on Portland Breakwater
2. Morris S., ca 1980, "Portland an Illustrated history", publisher unknown.
3. Trinity House Record, 1985.
4. Stevenson, D. A. "The World's Lighthouses Before 1820," 1959 Oxford University Press, Oxford.
5. "Hutchinson's History and Antiquities of the County of Dorset", 1881, Vol II, 3rd edn.
6. Dorset County Archives, Ph 609/2.
7. Davenport- Adams, W. H., "Lighthouses and Lightships" (1878).
8. Langmaid K., "The Sea Thine Enemy", 1966, Jarrolds, London.
9. Findlay, A. G., 1881, "A Description and List of the Lighthouses of the World", Richard Holmes Laurie, Fleet St., London, UK, 25th. edn.
10. Dorset County Archives, D/RWR/X16.
11. Trinity house Engineering, 52/39G.
12. Trinity House Engineering, 52/57.
13. Dorset County Archives, Copy 365/24.
14. Trinity House Engineering, 52/58.
15. Trinity House Engineering, 52/21.
16. Trinity House Engineering, 52/6.
17. Trinity House Engineering, 52/12.
OTHER SOURCES Parliamentary Papers, LXIII - 363 (216) 1863. Minutes of the Proceedings of the Institution of Civil Engineers, Vol. 57, 1879.

To obtain a free list of 'LIGHTHOUSES OF ENGLAND & WALES' booklets and the details of our 'NO OBLIGATION TO BUY', book club, send a S.A.E. to B&T PUBLICATIONS, 10 Orchard Way, Highfield, Southampton S017 1RD, UK.

To accompany this collection of 'LIGHTHOUSES OF ENGLAND AND WALES', the authors have compiled two special publications. The first booklet is titled 'BRITISH PHAROLOGY' and gives an easy to read insight into the Corporation of Trinity House, the Commissioners of Irish Lights, the Commissioners of the Northern Lights, Private Lighthouse owners, Royal Letter Patents and the services which are provided today. This booklet also gives an account of the designers and builders of the lighthouses around the coasts of the British Isles.

The second publication provides a detailed account of the various light sources, fuels, reflectors and optical apparatus, lanterns and fog warning systems and an insight to those designers and manufacturers who supplied these items. Titled 'TO LIGHT THEIR WAY', this booklet has been produced with many archive photos and pictorials, which have been provided by the various lighthouse authorities and by the author of 'PHAROS', Kenneth Sutton-Jones. This author has also assisted in a major way, by ensuring that the relative technical details are correct. This help has been greatly appreciated by the authors. Each of these booklets can be obtained from bookshops or direct from the publisher, (POST FREE IN UK).

Also available from B&T PUBLICATIONS: DataBase of the Lighthouses of Great Britain and Ireland. Full colour Windows (3.11 and 95) software. References and locations for over 350 lighthouses. Details of characteristic, fog signals, lat/long, type of tower, date established, history and sources of information. Enlarged and updated each year. Modify the database to suit your own needs. Comprehensive Search and Help functions. Suitable for PC computers with Windows 3.11 or 95 and VGA screen resolution and above. Requires 2Mb hard disk space and 3.5" floppy disk drive. Not suitable for Apple-MacIntosh computers.

For details of the membership for 'THE LIGHTHOUSE SOCIETY OF GREAT BRITAIN' send a s.a.e. to THE SECRETARY, Gravesend Cottage, Torpoint, Cornwall PL11 2LX, UK. Information is also available on the Internet at **http://www.soton.ac.uk/~kt1/**